GRUMPY CAT®

NO-IT-ALL

GRUMPY CAT®

NO -IT -ALL

EVERYTHING YOU NEED TO ~~KNOW~~ NO

SCHOLASTIC INC.

NO *Thanks to:*

Bryan, Tabatha, Chyrstal, and Elizabeth Bundesen, Ben Lashes, Heather Taylor, Kia Kamran, Julianne Freund, Molly Alward, Todd Thorson, Michael Morris, Wynn Rankin, Michelle Clair, Lia Brown, April Whitney, Albee Dalbotten, Ryan Cunningham, Liza Algar, Paul Myers, Peter Perez, Mike Adkins, Angela Bundesen, Betty Smith, Pokey, Shaggy, and Grumpy's Frienemies everywhere!

ISBN 978-0-545-92651-5

12 11 10 9 8 7 6 5 4 3 2 1   15 16 17 18 19 20/0

Printed in the U.S.A.   40

First Scholastic printing, December 2015

STOCK IMAGE CREDITS:
p. 48-9 Dream Master / Shutterstock.com

Dedicated to the most useful
word in the world:

NO

SAYING "YES" IS OVERRATED.

IF YOU REALLY WANT TO GET NOTHING DONE, JUST SAY ONE MAGIC WORD:

NO

THIS BOOK CONTAINS ALL OF MY LEAST FAVORITE THINGS. CONSIDER IT YOUR GUIDE TO EVERYTHING YOU NEED TO NO.

WHY NO?

WHEN YOU SAY YES

- ☺ PEOPLE SMILE
- ☺ CONVERSATIONS KEEP GOING
- ☺ YOU HAVE TO DO SOMETHING

WHEN YOU SAY NO

- ☹ PEOPLE FROWN (IF YOU'RE LUCKY)
- ☹ CONVERSATIONS END
- ☹ YOU HAVE TO DO NOTHING

WINNER: **NO**

NOW STOP ASKING QUESTIONS AND TAKE THE "NO-IT-ALL" OATH:

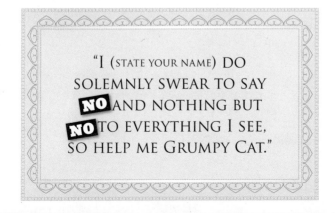

"I (STATE YOUR NAME) DO SOLEMNLY SWEAR TO SAY **NO** AND NOTHING BUT **NO** TO EVERYTHING I SEE, SO HELP ME GRUMPY CAT."

Positive Thinking

PROBLEM:

SEEING THE GLASS HALF FULL.

NO

Butterflies

You see a wonder of nature.
I SEE A STUPID FLYING BUG SHOWING OFF.

I LIKED YOU BETTER

IN THE COCOON.

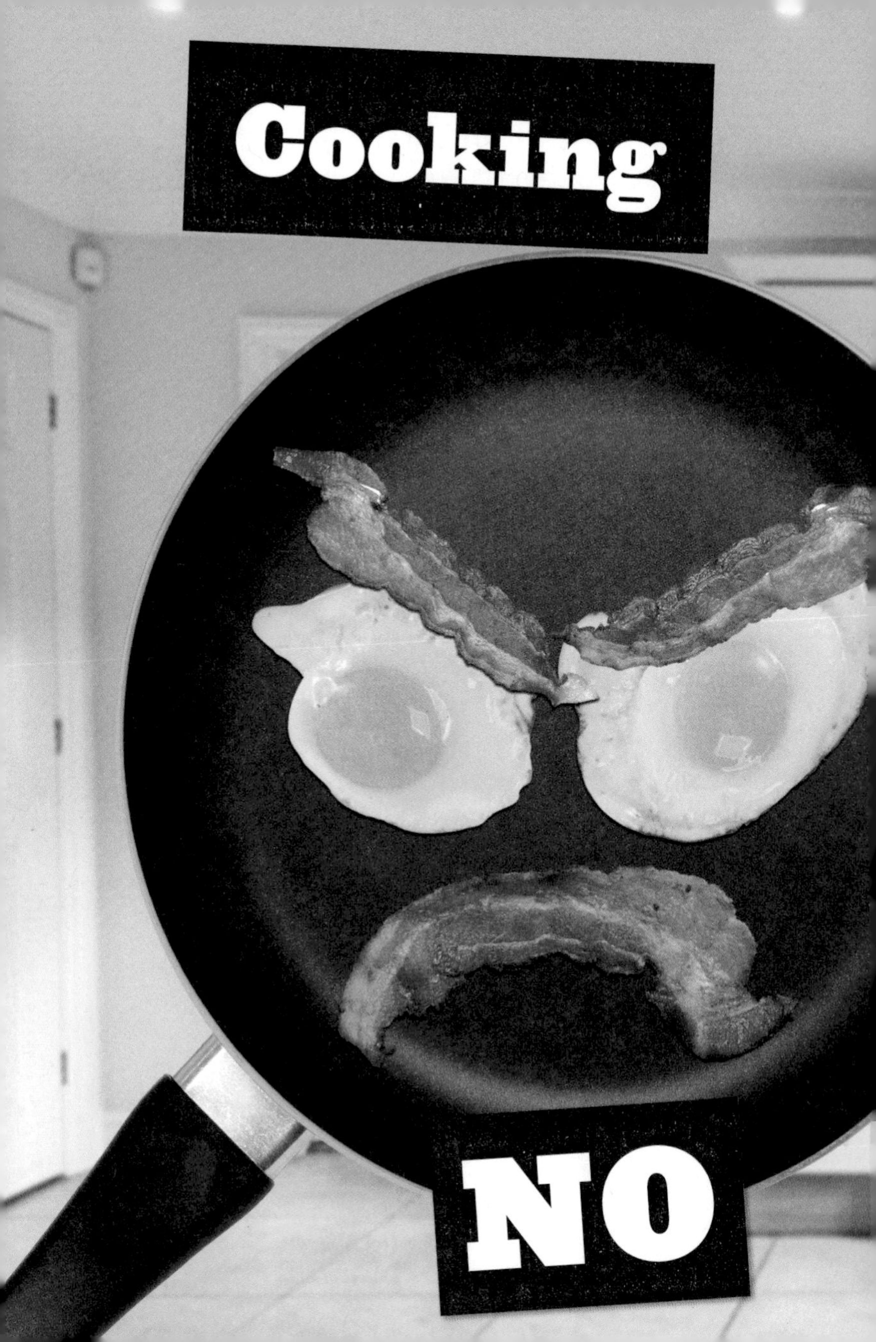
Cooking
NO

Flowers

NO

NO

NO

NO

**LESS POLLINATING
MORE STINGING.**

Holidays

NEW ADVENTURES

ARE THE WORST.

NO

THIS BABY IS OKAY, THOUGH.

Amusement Parks

GRUMPY'S
NO-LLER COASTER

NO

THIS BIRTHDAY IS OFFICIALLY CANCELLED.

Cuddling

YOU KEEP TRYING.

I KEEP SCRATCHING.

Toys

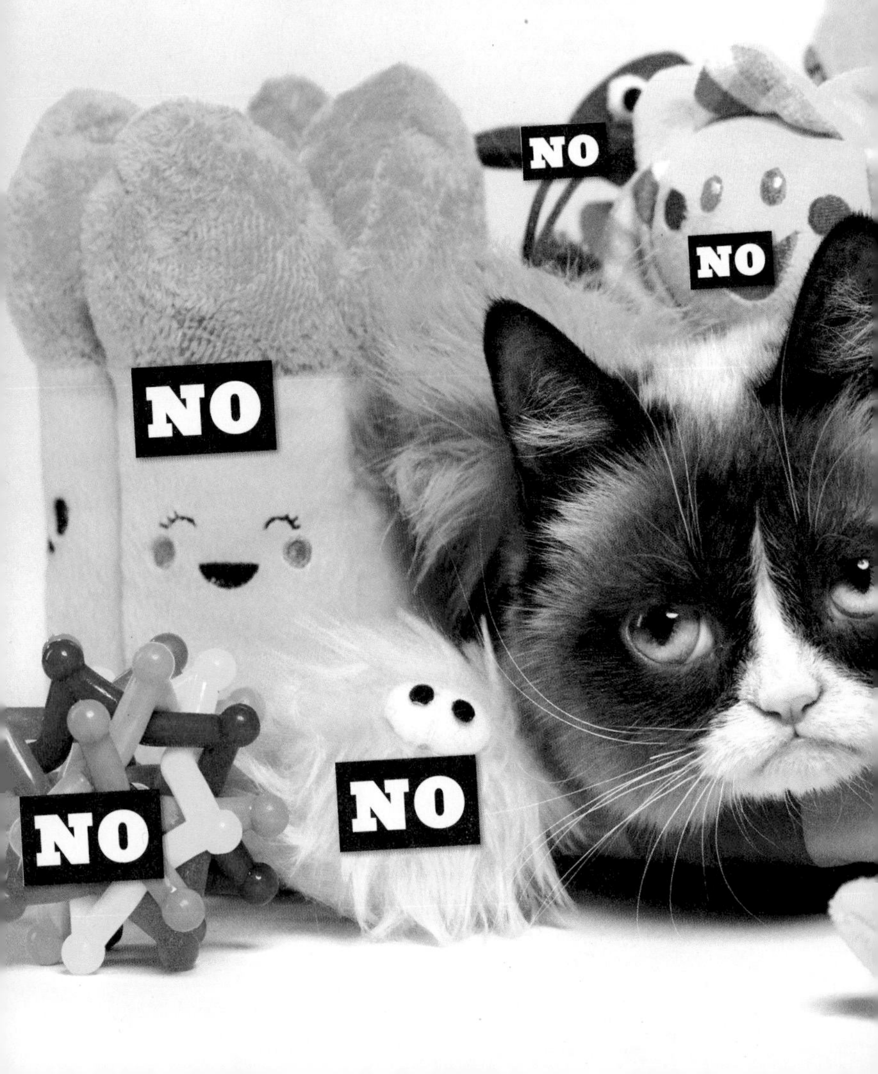

Days of the Week

EVERY NEW
BEGINNING

ENDS

SUNDAY

NO

SPORTS ARE ON, PROBABLY. I JUST REMIND MYSELF THAT HALF THE TEAMS LOSE.

MONDAY

OKAY, ACTUALLY.

EVERYONE IS MISERABLE. GOAL: MAKE EVERY DAY A MONDAY.

TUESDAY

NO

NOT MONDAY.

WEDNESDAY

NO

EVEN FURTHER FROM MONDAY.

THURSDAY

NO

ALMOST FRIDAY. PEOPLE SEEM . . . HOPEFUL? UGH.

FRIDAY

NO

THE WORST.

SATURDAY

NO

I REFUSE TO OPEN MY EYES ON THIS DAY BUT I ASSUME IT'S TERRIBLE, TOO.

Swimming

Grumpy

NOTHING IMPOR

Grumpy Cat is on a mission to "NO" everything.

NO
Gazette

OUR OWN BUSINESS?

EST • 2012

...NT HAPPENED

...RUMPY CAT WALKS OUT OF INTERVIEW

...o bored to continue," says World-Famous
...owning Feline.

SMILES MUST BE STOPPED

says International Committee on the Elimination of Smiles.

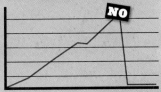

Source: I.C.E.S.

Movies

Exercise

EXCEPTION:

RUNNING AWAY FROM SOMEONE ANNOYING.

Presents

Driving

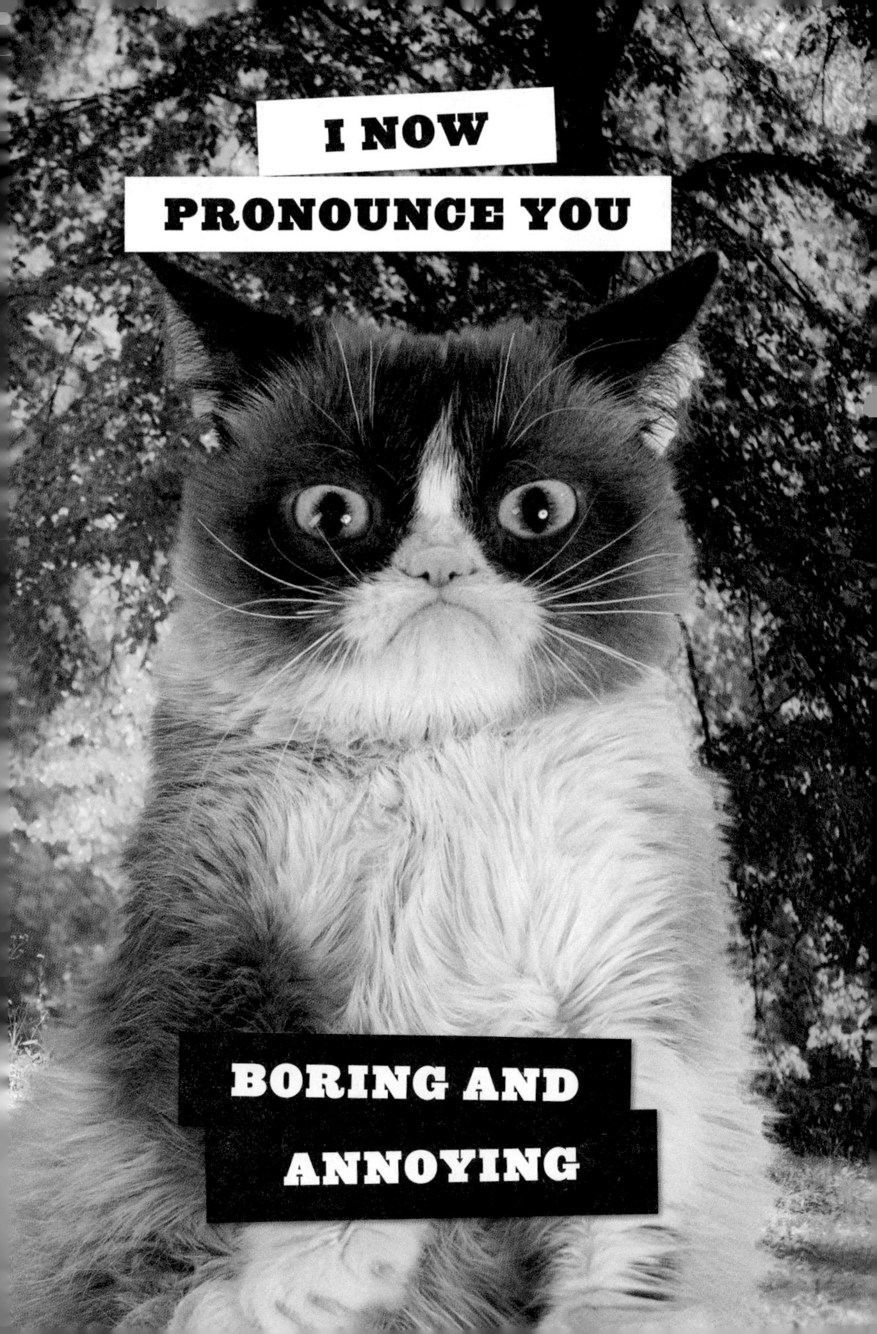
I NOW
PRONOUNCE YOU
BORING AND
ANNOYING

Texting

Fashion

THEN

NO

realgrumpycat

1hr

🗨 **realgrumpycat** No

History

NO

NO

NO

NO

NO

NO

Music

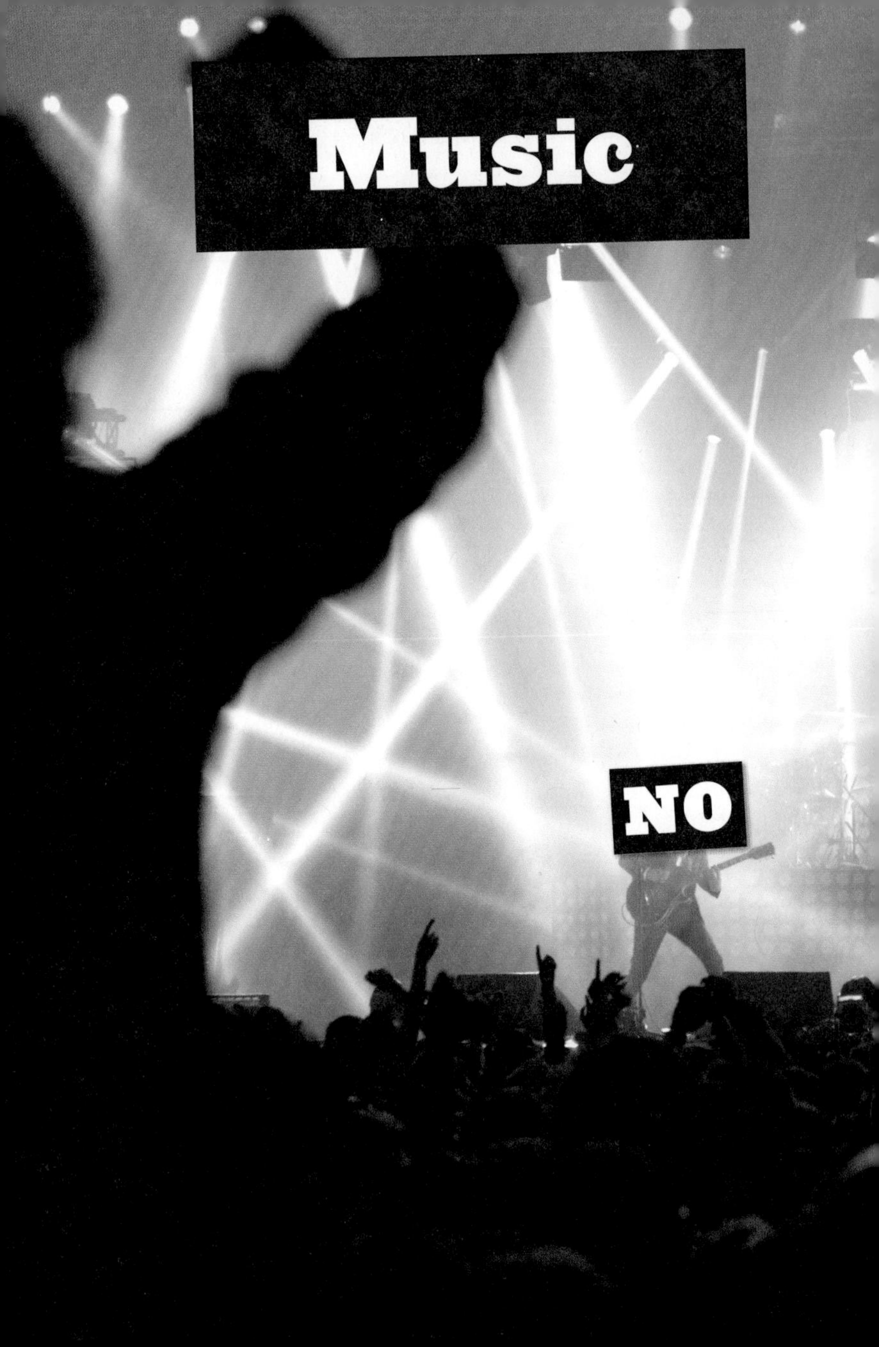

NO

Television

Sequels

GRUMPY CAT

GRUMPY CAT

NO

A **GRUMPY** BOOK

DISGRUNTLED TIPS AND ACTIVITIES
DESIGNED TO PUT A FROWN ON YOUR FACE

The **GRUMPY GUIDE** *to LIFE*

NO

OBSERVATIONS
by GRUMPY CAT

Kittens

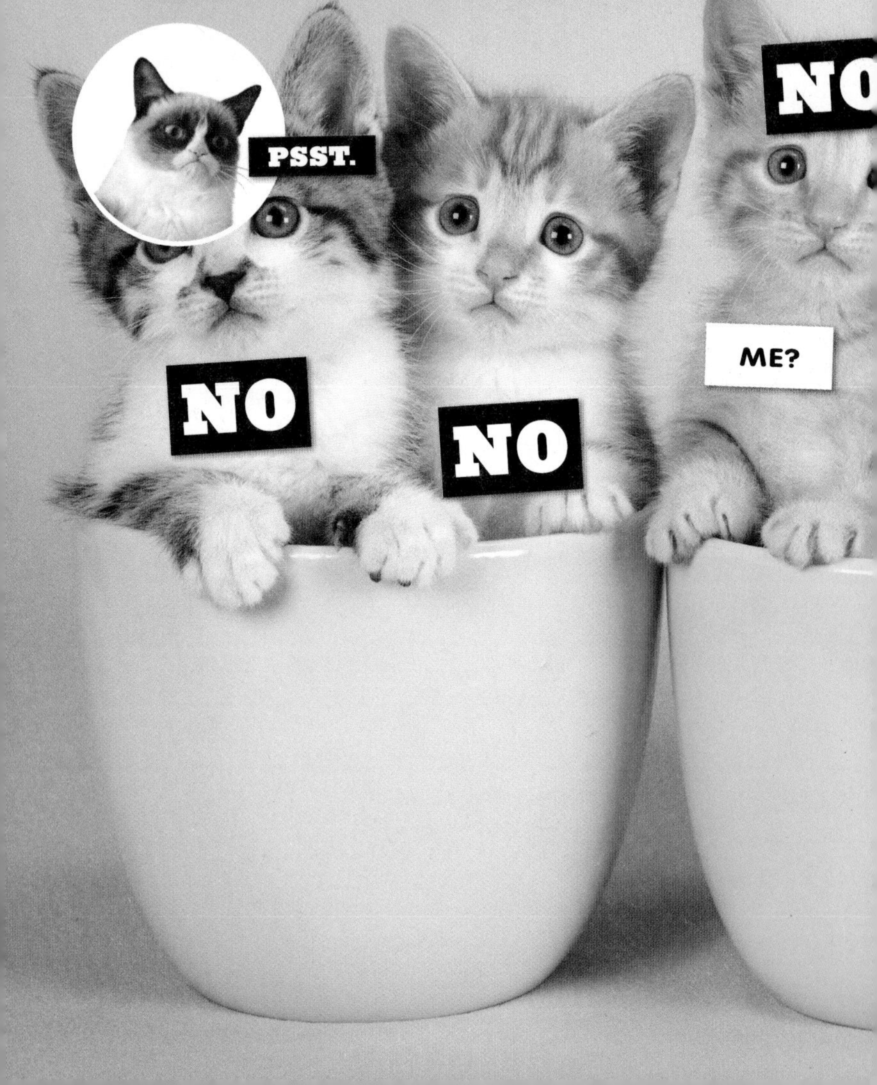

NO NO NO

YOU'RE TERRIBLE.

NO

NO

THIS IS WHAT
A BASKET OF
BAD BREATH
LOOKS LIKE.

Any Cute Animals, Really

DUCKLING

NO

KOALAS

NO

NO

HEDGEHOG

NO

The Internet

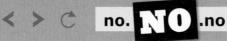

no. **NO** .no

NO 🔍

THINKING OF YOU

IT'S TERRIBLE

IF YOU'RE HAPPY AND YOU KNOW IT

GET AWAY FROM ME

FROWN AND THE WHOLE WORLD FROWNS WITH YOU.

I HAD FUN O

IT WAS AWF

NOgle

QUIT WHILE YOU'RE AHEAD.
Quit while you're behind. The important thing to remember is this: **QUIT.**

THERE'S NO "I" IN TEAM

THERE'S NO "YOU" EITHER

PUT YOUR BEST **FROWN** FORWARD

EENY

MEENY

MINY

NO

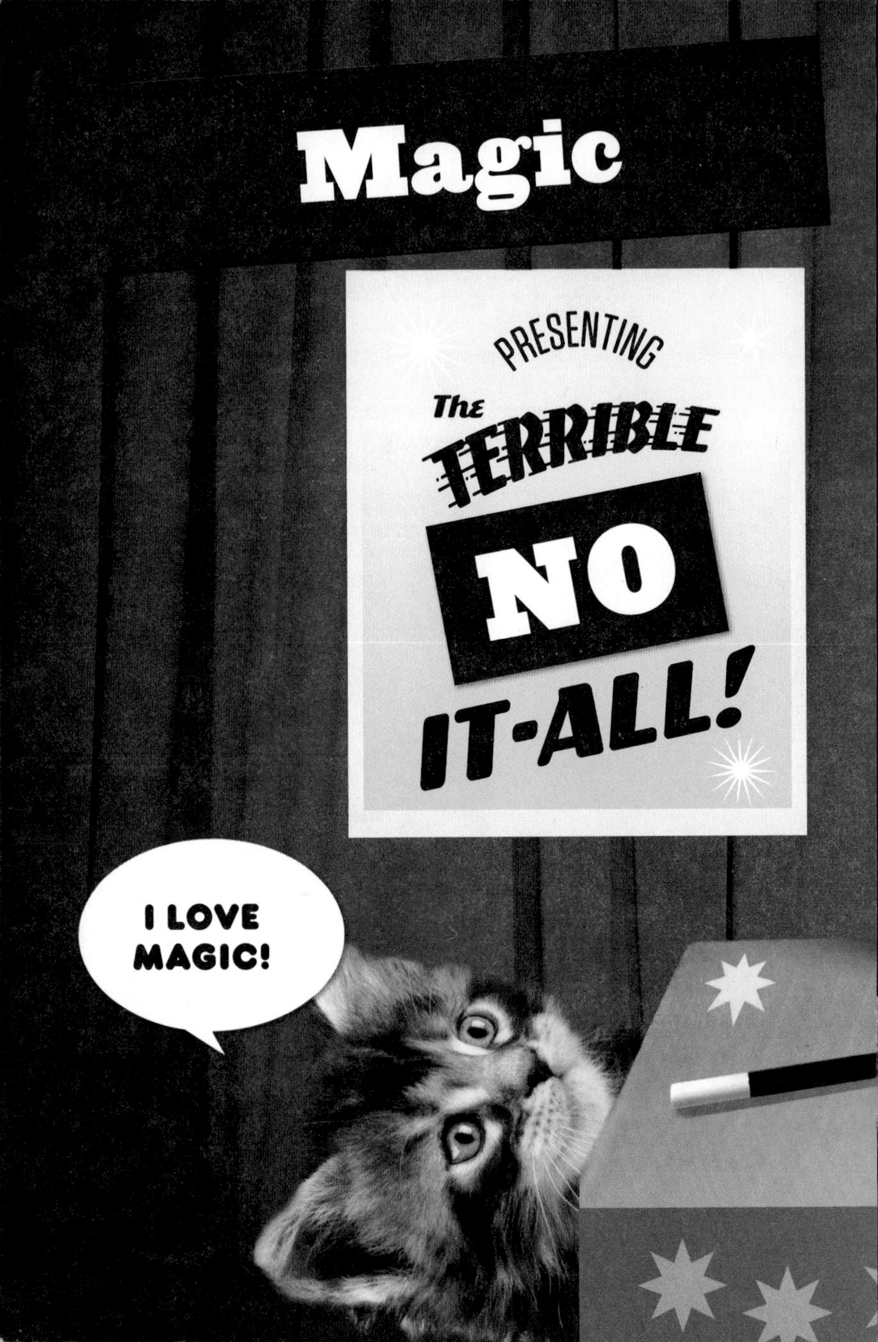
Magic
PRESENTING
The TERRIBLE
NO
IT-ALL!
I LOVE MAGIC!

Balloons

NO

THIS DID NOT END WELL.

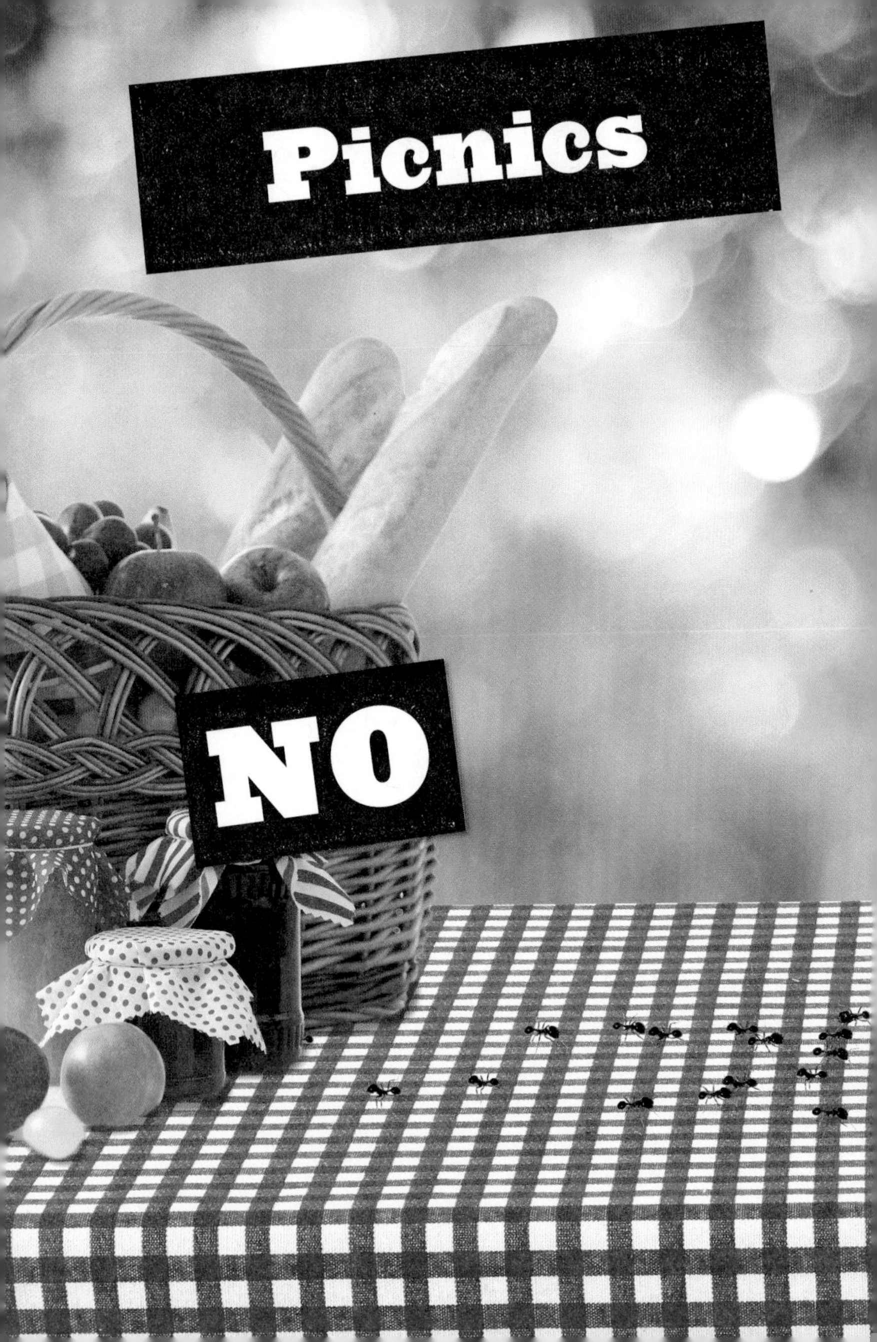
Picnics
NO

GET ME OUT OF HERE.

WAIT. I SHOULD BE SQUISHING YOU.

Fairy Tales

Once upon a

School

NO

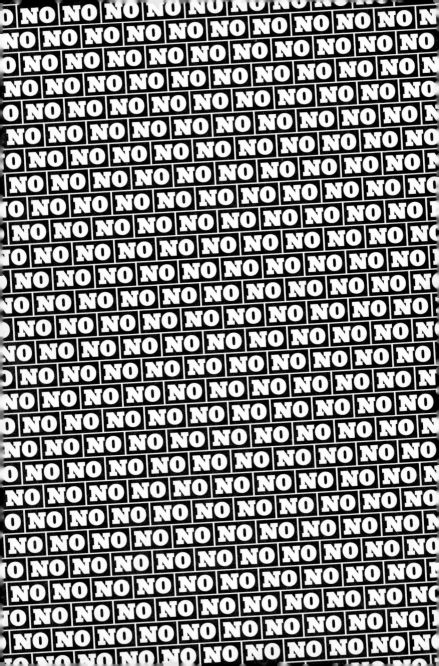